Make a wish, Witzy!

Yay, team!

Hi, I'm Lulla the musical bunny!

Lulla does the hula.

What's up, Witzy?

Boof listens.

Where are you flying to, Tickle?

How do you do, Peek-a-boo?

What will Witzy do today?

A beautiful skiprope!

All for me?

Princess Lulla likes to dance with her friends!

Smooch!

Pretty as a princess.

Flootie loves daffodils.

Look at all the beautiful flowers, Patches!

Lulla loves balloons.

Let's go explore, Peek-a-boo!

Huggle snuggle!

Good kick, Patches!

Here we go!

Hello, Peek-a-boo!

Hello, Zoom Zoom!

Ready to roll!

Patches leads the band.

Watch out for Ellie Funt!

Witzy looks for one more lightning bug.

Good day to you, butterflies!

Boof and Witzy see shapes in the clouds.

A summer song.

Lots of Tickles!

Tickle bugs love Witzy.

Lulla jumps over a wishing puff!

Lulla sparkles!

It's fun to cloud-shape hunt!

Peek-a-boo is a good artist.

Where are you going with that wishing puff?

Give me a W!

Hop to it!

What a warm, cozy blanket!

Fireflies light the way!

Rah! Rah! Rah!

"Let's go play!" says Lulla.

Lulla is a musical bunny.

Colors in flight!

Bounce-bounce-bounce!

Well, hello!

Flootie and Peek-a-boo visit the Tickle bugs.

Lulla makes a lovely princess.

Wait for me, Flootie!

A sweet serenade.

Peek-a-boo has a snack.

Patches is a kind giraffe.

Patches can reach the tallest things.

Would you like a cookie, Tickle?

Thank you, Witzy!

Good-night hugs.

Witzy and Lulla share a story.

Such a long climb!

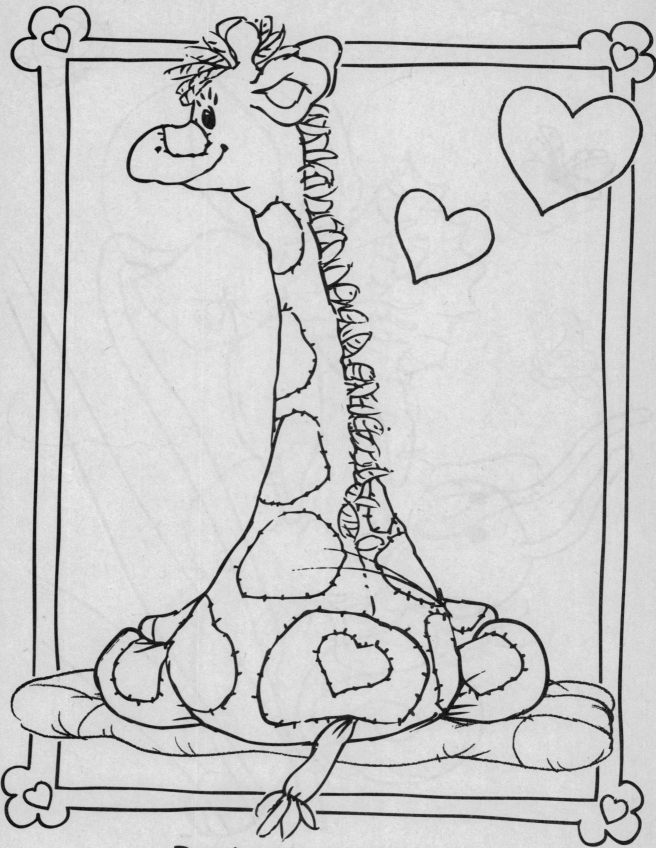

Patches has a special
heart patch on his back.

Up, up, and away!

Little flutter-by friends!

Lulla has sweet friends.

It's a beautiful day in Witzy's backyard.